Carnedd Lewellyn N.W. 3469

Ben Mou N.B. 3500

Crudchen Ben N.B. 3400

Snowden the Highest Hill in N.W. 3571

Schehallion N.B. 3500

Carnedd David N.W. 3427

High Point 366   Low Point 3092

llyn 3053 berland

Sea Fell Cumberland the Highest Hill in England

Skiddaw Cumb.d 3082

Cross Fell Cumb.d 2901

Brecon, the highest in S.W.

The Pillar Cumb. 2893

Bow Fell Cumb.d 2911

Saddleback Cumb.d 2787

Cheviot N.B. 2653

Grasmere Fell Cumb.d 2756

Coniston Fell Lancas. 2577

Cadir Terwyn N.W. 2563

Cradle S.W. 2545

Dunrias N.B. 2409

Capellant S.W. 2394

Hedgehope Northumb. 2347

Plynlimmon S.W. 2463

Shunner Fell Yorksh. 2329

Whernside in Ingleton Fells Yorksh. 2384

Water Crag Yorksh. 2186

Queensbury Hill N.B. 2259

Carn Fell 2243 Yorksh.

Kilpope Law Durham 2190

Whern Kettlewell Yorksh.

Forest 163

Ingleborough Yorksh. 2361   Pennagent Yorksh. 2270

9 Standards Westmorland 2136

Dwygau Brecon 2071

High Peak Cumber.d 210

Black Comb Cumber.d 1919

Holm

Snca Fell Isle of Man 2004

Yorkshire Trovert

"Pendal, Ingleboro and Pennigent Are the Highest Hills between Scotland & Trent"

North Berule Isle of Man

Derbysh. 1859

Beacon 1792

Gerwyn Gioch N.W. 1723

Pendal Hill Lancashire 1803

Axedge Derbyshire 1751

Longmount Forest Salop 1674

Llangunor S.W. 1659

Dunkerry Beacon the Highest Hill West of England

Mynydd's Marc Monmouthsh. 1568

Penmaen Mawr N.W. 1540

Rippon Torr Devon 1549

Malvern 1444

Elden Hills N.B. 1364

Wrekin Salop 1320

Mamtorr Derbysh. 1300 one of the Wonders of the Peak

Stow Hill Herefordshire

Black Hambledown Yorksh. 1246

Broadway Beacon 1086

Weaver Hill Staffordshire

Butte Devon

Bradley Knoll

Moeltra Afst Denbighsh. 1031

White Horse Hill Berk 803

Leith's Hill Surry 993

Botley Hill Surry 830

Hind Hill 992 Surry

Wendover

Epwell Hill Oxfordsh. 836

Nettlebed Windmill Oxfordsh. 770

Rooks Hill 702 Surry

Hollingborn Kent 616

Shotover Oxford 599

Stockbridge Hants 690

Banstead Downs Surry 576

Norwood Hills 380

Shooters Hill 446 Kent

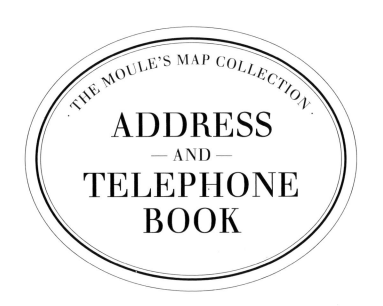

THE MOULE'S MAP COLLECTION

ADDRESS

— AND —

TELEPHONE

BOOK

STUDIO
DESIGNS

FIRST PUBLISHED IN 1991 BY STUDIO DESIGNS,
AN IMPRINT OF STUDIO EDITIONS LIMITED,
PRINCESS HOUSE, 50 EASTCASTLE STREET,
LONDON W1N 7AP, ENGLAND.

REPRINTED 1992, 1995

COPYRIGHT © STUDIO DESIGNS 1991

ALL RIGHTS RESERVED. NO PART OF THIS PUBLICATION MAY BE REPRODUCED
STORED IN A RETRIEVAL SYSTEM, OR TRANSMITTED, IN ANY FORM OR BY ANY
MEANS, ELECTRONIC, MECHANICAL, PHOTOCOPYING, RECORDING OR OTHERWISE,
WITHOUT THE PRIOR PERMISSION OF THE COPYRIGHT HOLDER.

PRINTED AND BOUND IN SPAIN

THE MAPS USED IN THIS PUBLICATION ARE TAKEN FROM THE COUNTY
MAPS OF OLD ENGLAND BY THOMAS MOULE, PUBLISHED 1990 BY STUDIO
EDITIONS LIMITED, LONDON WITH AN INTRODUCTION BY RODERICK
BARRON, ORIGINALLY PUBLISHED IN 1830 AS *THE ENGLISH COUNTIES
DELINEATED*. THE MAPS HAVE BEEN COLOURED FOR THIS WORK.

THE TEXT FOR THE PUBLICATION WAS FIRST PUBLISHED IN *BARCLAY'S
COMPLETE AND UNIVERSAL DICTIONARY*, 1842, WITH THE INTRODUCTION
TAKEN FROM RODERICK BARRON'S INTRODUCTION TO *THE COUNTY MAPS
OF OLD ENGLAND*.

THOMAS MOULE

In a modern society haunted by the spectre of industrialism, urban decline and environmental destruction, we can, like the early Victorian, appreciate Thomas Moule's maps for their old-fashioned quaintness and superb artistry. It is these qualities which have made Moule's work so popular with map collectors, scholars and historians.

For more so than many other works these maps constitute one of the finest visual records of the profound changes which occurred in early nineteenth century England when on the framework of an ancient county landscape was built the new age of industrialism.

The 1830s was a watershed for England. The economic and social infrastructure was changed forever. New industries, such as textiles and iron, led to massive population movements from rural areas to the rapidly expanding towns. Between 1821 and 1831 Liverpool, for example, grew by forty-six per cent and during the first half of the nineteenth century London grew at a rate of 100,000 people per decade; London was becoming the hub of a new world empire.

The nineteenth century was the great age of coach travel and this was paralleled by improvements in road systems. It was also the age of steam; steam to drive the wheels of industry and also the engines of trains. For the first time ever parts of the country which had previously been accessible to only the hardiest and most seasoned traveller came within the reach of even the most casual of 'tourists'. A mass market, relatively well-educated and now mobile, provided a new impetus to the art of mapmaking. And the maps of Thomas Moule are one of the crowning achievements of this revival.

Moule wanted to make his maps within the reach of 'every class' and with this in mind his maps were first published in parts at a price of '1s plain or 1s 6d coloured'. The industrial revolution had also made it possible to produce maps and atlases in greater numbers and at a lower cost. Innovations in plate making and paper making also worked to Moule's advantage.

When first published in atlas form by George Virtue in 1837 as the *English Counties Delineated* it contained fifty-seven maps of England and Wales, of inland navigation, of the English counties and town plans of London, Bath, Boston, Portsmouth, Plymouth and the Isles of Thanet, Wight and Man. The maps were constantly being revised not only to suit the publisher's discretion but to keep the maps up to date.

Two of the most significant factors which made revising necessary was the need to include information on the new constituencies (a result of the Reform Bill of 1832) and the number of MPs returned to Parliament, and the expansion of the railway network. The new mass market of railway travellers posed immediate problems for mapmakers such as Moule. Maps became obsolete as soon as they were engraved. Moule's publisher was not worried about it, issuing both old stock and newly revised maps simultaneously. Later Moule's maps were issued to accompany the 'Complete and Universal English Dictionary by the Reverend James Barclay … Revised by Henry W. Dewhurst Esq. F.E.S. L.'. The maps were given an even wider audience when they were bound into Hume and Smollett's work, *The History of England*.

George Virtue was aware of the lasting popularity of Moule's maps. Their lifespan of over forty years was much longer than almost any other series of Victorian maps. Their elaborate and decorative style, a synthesis of art and cartography, sets them apart from most other maps of the period, whose plain unembellished style owed much to the pioneering work of the Ordnance Survey.

One recurring feature of these beautifully decorative maps is their high Gothic style – numerous maps are set within Gothic pilasters, recesses and alcoves complete with armorial bearings and coats of arms. As an authority on the history of architecture Moule must have been aware of the great revival in Gothic architecture popularized by Auguste Pugin. This was a movement opposed to the new industrial and capitalistic age, a movement that looked back to the Middle Ages, to the roots of English society in its countryside and its history. This movement reached its climax in the year of Moule's death, 1851.

But not only is it the artistry which makes these maps so enduring. Moule was truly fascinated with the past and in bringing it alive and had a deep-seated interest in local history, local anecdotes and the beauties of the landscape. He was aware that there was a demand for this sort of information but he combined it with information on the 'splendid remains of Antiquity'. In preparing for this work Moule claimed with great pride that he had 'visited every county in England excepting only Derbyshire and Cornwall'.

IMPORTANT NUMBERS/FAMILY

Name

Telephone

Name

Telephone

Name

Telephone

Name

Telephone

Name

Telephone

Name

Telephone

Name

Telephone

Name

Telephone

Name

Telephone

Name

Telephone

Name

Telephone

Name

Telephone

Name

Telephone

Name

Telephone

Name

Telephone

Name

Telephone

Name

Telephone

Name

Telephone

Name

Telephone

Name

Telephone

Name

Telephone

Name

Telephone

Name

Telephone

Name

Telephone

IMPORTANT NUMBERS/EMERGENCY

Name

Telephone

Night

Emergency

Name

Telephone

Night

Emergency

Name

Telephone

Night

Emergency

Name

Telephone

Night

Emergency

Name

Telephone

Night

Emergency

Name

Telephone

Night

Emergency

Name

Telephone

Night

Emergency

Name

Telephone

Night

Emergency

Name

Telephone

Night

Emergency

Name

Telephone

Night

Emergency

Name

Telephone

Night

Emergency

Name

Telephone

Night

Emergency

Services and Suppliers

Name

Telephone

Special Notes

Name

Telephone

Special Notes

Name

Telephone

Special Notes

Name

Telephone

Special Notes

Name

Telephone

Special Notes

Name

Telephone

Special Notes

Name

Telephone

Special Notes

Name

Telephone

Special Notes

Name

Telephone

Special Notes

Name

Telephone

Special Notes

Name

Telephone

Special Notes

Name

Telephone

Special Notes

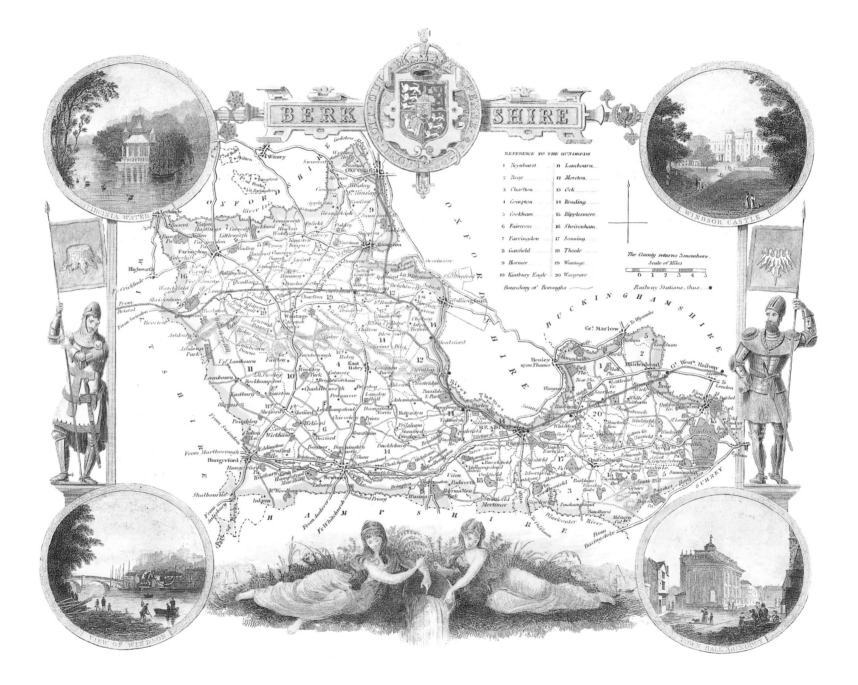

BERK SHIRE

REFERENCE TO THE HUNDREDS

1	Beynhurst	11	Lambourn
2	Bray	12	Moreton
3	Charlton	13	Ock
4	Compton	14	Reading
5	Cookham	15	Ripplesmere
6	Faircross	16	Shrivenham
7	Farringdon	17	Sonning
8	Ganfield	18	Theale
9	Hormer	19	Wantage
10	Kintbury Eagle	20	Wargrave

The County returns 3 members.

Scale of Miles

0 1 2 3 4 5

Boundary of Boroughs

Railway Stations, thus

VIRGINIA WATER

WINDSOR CASTLE

VIEW OF WINDSOR

TOWN HALL, ABINGDON

NAME/ADDRESS

Name   Address

Telephone

Facsimile

                                         Post Code

Name   Address

Telephone

Facsimile

                                         Post Code

Name   Address

Telephone

Facsimile

                                         Post Code

Name   Address

Telephone

Facsimile

                                         Post Code

Name   Address

Telephone

Facsimile

                                         Post Code

NAME /ADDRESS

Name   Address

Telephone

Facsimile

                                            Post Code

Name   Address

Telephone

Facsimile

                                            Post Code

Name   Address

Telephone

Facsimile

                                            Post Code

Name   Address

Telephone

Facsimile

                                            Post Code

Name   Address

Telephone

Facsimile

                                            Post Code

NAME /ADDRESS

Name

Telephone

Facsimile

Address

Post Code

Name

Telephone

Facsimile

Address

Post Code

Name

Telephone

Facsimile

Address

Post Code

Name

Telephone

Facsimile

Address

Post Code

Name

Telephone

Facsimile

Address

Post Code

REFERENCE of HUNDREDS

Broxton ......1. Macclesfield ..4.
Bucklow ......2. Nantwich ......5.
Edisbury ......3. Northwich ....6.
Wirrall ......7.

County returns 4 Members

Scale of Miles
0 1 2 4 6 8 10

Railway Stations, thus .

IRISH SEA

RIVER MERSEY

RIVER DEE

FLINTSHIRE

DENBIGHSHIRE

LANCASHIRE

DERBYSHIRE

STAFFORDSHIRE

YORKSHIRE

New Brighton
Wallasey
Seacombe
Moreton
Bidstone
Lit. Meols
Upton
Frankby
Birkenhead
West Kirby
Wood Ch.
Tranmere
Irby
Grange
Gt. Meols
Hoylake
Hilbre I.
Thurstaston
Heswall
Barnston
Bromborough
Poulton
Bebington
Gr. Neston
Lit. Neston
Ness
Burton
Ledsham
Parkgate
Leighton
Puddington
Shotwick
Capenhurst
Mollington
Upton
Gr. Saughall
New Beaconcliffe
Blacon
Saltney

LIVERPOOL

Warrington
Runcorn
Frodsham
Helsby
Ince
Elton
Thornton
Manley
Delamere
Kelsall
Tarvin
Ashton
Mouldsworth
Dunham
Christleton
Huntington
Rowton
Waverton
Saighton
Aldford
Churton
Coddington
Stretton
Clutton
Crewe Hall
Shocklach
Chorlton
Malpas
Cholmondeley
Wrenbury
Marbury

CHESTER

Tarporley
Nantwich
Sandbach
Middlewich
Northwich
Knutsford
Altringham
Bowdon
Stockport
Manchester
Stayley Brigs
Ashton under Lyne
Macclesfield
Congleton

Chester to Manchester Railway

CHESHIRE.

CHESTER CATHEDRAL

EATON HALL

Name /Address

Name

Telephone

Facsimile

Address

Post Code

Name

Telephone

Facsimile

Address

Post Code

Name

Telephone

Facsimile

Address

Post Code

Name

Telephone

Facsimile

Address

Post Code

Name

Telephone

Facsimile

Address

Post Code

NAME/ADDRESS

Name _____   Address _____

Telephone _____   _____

Facsimile _____

                                           Post Code _____

Name _____   Address _____

Telephone _____   _____

Facsimile _____

                                           Post Code _____

Name _____   Address _____

Telephone _____   _____

Facsimile _____

                                           Post Code _____

Name _____   Address _____

Telephone _____   _____

Facsimile _____

                                           Post Code _____

Name _____   Address _____

Telephone _____   _____

Facsimile _____

                                           Post Code _____

NAME /ADDRESS

Name

Telephone

Facsimile

Address

Post Code

Name

Telephone

Facsimile

Address

Post Code

Name

Telephone

Facsimile

Address

Post Code

Name

Telephone

Facsimile

Address

Post Code

Name

Telephone

Facsimile

Address

Post Code

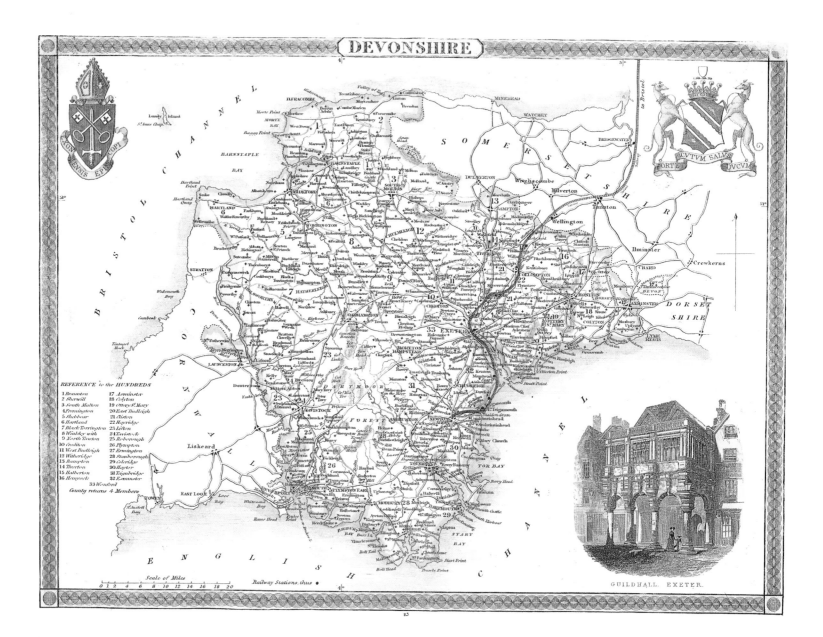

DEVONSHIRE

BRISTOL CHANNEL

SOMERSETSHIRE

DORSET SHIRE

CORNWALL

ENGLISH CHANNEL

BARNSTAPLE BAY

TOR BAY

START BAY

REFERENCE to the HUNDREDS

1 Braunton
2 Sherwill
3 South Molton
4 Fremington
5 Shebbear
6 Hartland
7 Black Torrington
8 Winkley with
9 North Tawton
10 Crediton
11 West Budleigh
12 Witheridge
13 Bampton
14 Tiverton
15 Halberton
16 Hemyock
17 Axminster
18 Colyton
19 Ottery St Mary
20 East Budleigh
21 Cliston
22 Hayridge
23 Lifton
24 Tavistock
25 Roborough
26 Plympton
27 Ermington
28 Stanborough
29 Coleridge
30 Haytor
31 Teignbridge
32 Exminster
33 Wonford

County returns 4 Members

Scale of Miles
0 1 2 4 6 8 10 12 14 16 18 20

Railway Stations, thus ●

GUILDHALL, EXETER.

NAME /ADDRESS

Name _____

Telephone _____

Facsimile _____

Address _____

_____

Post Code _____

Name _____

Telephone _____

Facsimile _____

Address _____

_____

Post Code _____

Name _____

Telephone _____

Facsimile _____

Address _____

_____

Post Code _____

Name _____

Telephone _____

Facsimile _____

Address _____

_____

Post Code _____

Name _____

Telephone _____

Facsimile _____

Address _____

_____

Post Code _____

Name /Address

Name

Telephone

Facsimile

Address

Post Code

Name

Telephone

Facsimile

Address

Post Code

Name

Telephone

Facsimile

Address

Post Code

Name

Telephone

Facsimile

Address

Post Code

Name

Telephone

Facsimile

Address

Post Code

NAME /ADDRESS

Name

Telephone

Facsimile

Address

Post Code

Name

Telephone

Facsimile

Address

Post Code

Name

Telephone

Facsimile

Address

Post Code

Name

Telephone

Facsimile

Address

Post Code

Name

Telephone

Facsimile

Address

Post Code

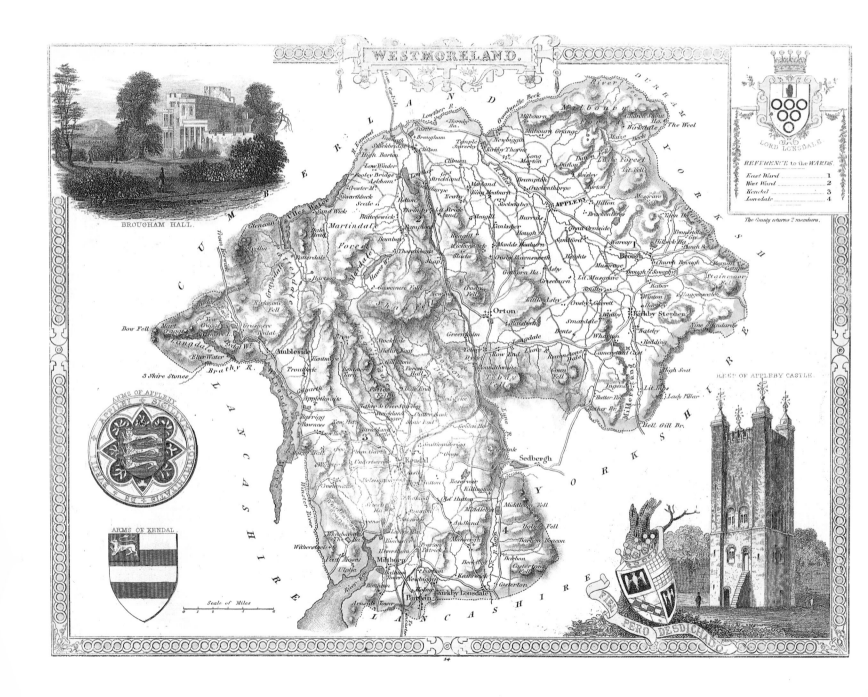

WESTMORELAND.

BROUGHAM HALL.

LORD LONSDALE.

The County returns 2 members.

SIGILLVM COMVNITATIS DE APPLEBY · ARMS OF APPLEBY

ARMS OF KENDAL.

KEEP OF APPLEBY CASTLE.

Scale of Miles

FIEL PERO DESDICHADO

NAME /ADDRESS

Name _____

Telephone _____

Facsimile _____

Address _____

_____

Post Code _____

Name _____

Telephone _____

Facsimile _____

Address _____

_____

Post Code _____

Name _____

Telephone _____

Facsimile _____

Address _____

_____

Post Code _____

Name _____

Telephone _____

Facsimile _____

Address _____

_____

Post Code _____

Name _____

Telephone _____

Facsimile _____

Address _____

_____

Post Code _____

Name/Address

Name _____   Address _____

Telephone _____   _____

Facsimile _____   _____

_____   Post Code _____

Name _____   Address _____

Telephone _____   _____

Facsimile _____   _____

_____   Post Code _____

Name _____   Address _____

Telephone _____   _____

Facsimile _____   _____

_____   Post Code _____

Name _____   Address _____

Telephone _____   _____

Facsimile _____   _____

_____   Post Code _____

Name _____   Address _____

Telephone _____   _____

Facsimile _____   _____

_____   Post Code _____

NAME /ADDRESS

Name

Telephone

Facsimile

Address

Post Code

Name

Telephone

Facsimile

Address

Post Code

Name

Telephone

Facsimile

Address

Post Code

Name

Telephone

Facsimile

Address

Post Code

Name

Telephone

Facsimile

Address

Post Code

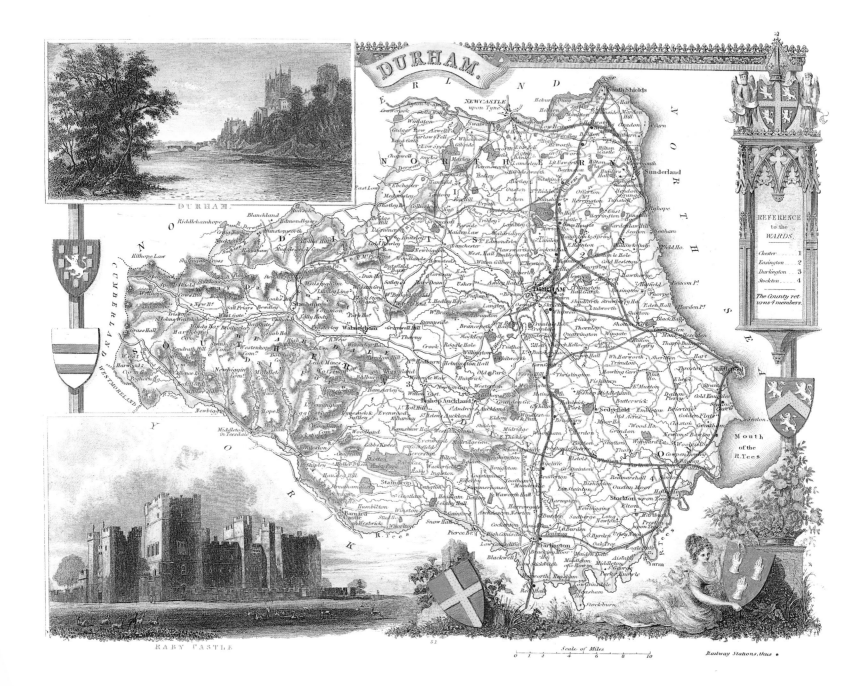

DURHAM

DURHAM

RABY CASTLE

REFERENCE
to the
WARDS.

Chester 1
Easington 2
Darlington 3
Stockton 4

The County returns 4 members.

Scale of Miles

0 1 2   4   6   8   10

Railway Stations, thus •

NAME /ADDRESS

Name _____

Telephone _____

Facsimile _____

Address _____

_____

Post Code _____

Name _____

Telephone _____

Facsimile _____

Address _____

_____

Post Code _____

Name _____

Telephone _____

Facsimile _____

Address _____

_____

Post Code _____

Name _____

Telephone _____

Facsimile _____

Address _____

_____

Post Code _____

Name _____

Telephone _____

Facsimile _____

Address _____

_____

Post Code _____

NAME / ADDRESS

Name _____   Address _____

Telephone _____   _____

Facsimile _____   _____

_____   Post Code _____

Name _____   Address _____

Telephone _____   _____

Facsimile _____   _____

_____   Post Code _____

Name _____   Address _____

Telephone _____   _____

Facsimile _____   _____

_____   Post Code _____

Name _____   Address _____

Telephone _____   _____

Facsimile _____   _____

_____   Post Code _____

Name _____   Address _____

Telephone _____   _____

Facsimile _____   _____

_____   Post Code _____

NAME /ADDRESS

Name _____

Telephone _____

Facsimile _____

Address _____

_____

Post Code _____

Name _____

Telephone _____

Facsimile _____

Address _____

_____

Post Code _____

Name _____

Telephone _____

Facsimile _____

Address _____

_____

Post Code _____

Name _____

Telephone _____

Facsimile _____

Address _____

_____

Post Code _____

Name _____

Telephone _____

Facsimile _____

Address _____

_____

Post Code _____

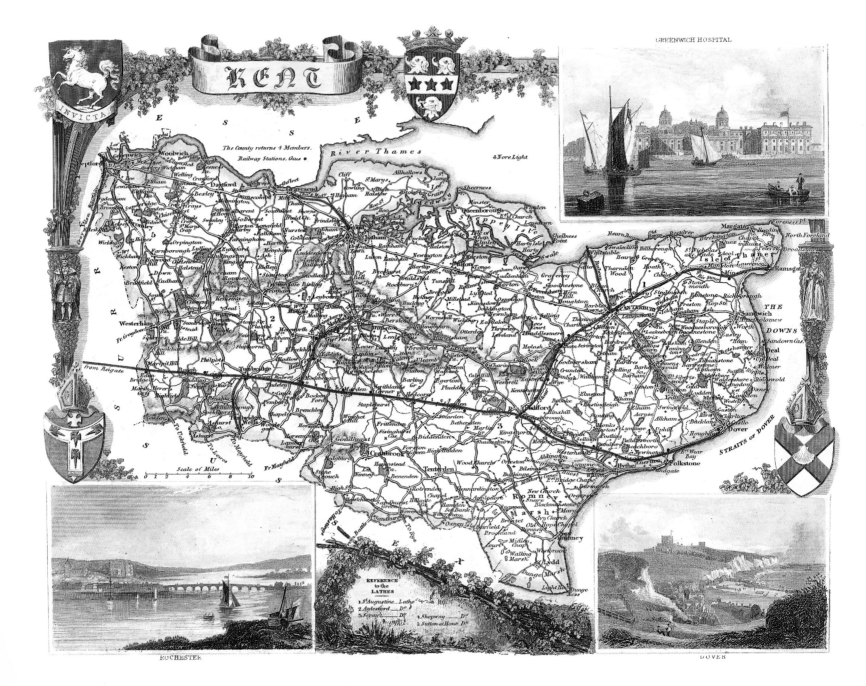

KENT

INVICTA

GREENWICH HOSPITAL

ESSEX

River Thames

The County returns 4 Members.
Railway Stations, thus ●

☆ Nore Light

SURREY

SUSSEX

Scale of Miles

THE DOWNS

STRAITS OF DOVER

ROMNEY MARSH

REFERENCE
to the
LATHES
1. St. Augustine.....Lathe
2. Aylesford.......D.º
3. Scray's........D.º
4. Shepway........D.º
5. Sutton at Hone D.º

ROCHESTER

DOVER

NAME/ADDRESS

Name

Telephone

Facsimile

Address

Post Code

Name

Telephone

Facsimile

Address

Post Code

Name

Telephone

Facsimile

Address

Post Code

Name

Telephone

Facsimile

Address

Post Code

Name

Telephone

Facsimile

Address

Post Code

NAME /ADDRESS

Name _____   Address _____

Telephone _____   _____

Facsimile _____   _____

_____   Post Code _____

_____

Name _____   Address _____

Telephone _____   _____

Facsimile _____   _____

_____   Post Code _____

_____

Name _____   Address _____

Telephone _____   _____

Facsimile _____   _____

_____   Post Code _____

_____

Name _____   Address _____

Telephone _____   _____

Facsimile _____   _____

_____   Post Code _____

_____

Name _____   Address _____

Telephone _____   _____

Facsimile _____   _____

_____   Post Code _____

Name /Address

Name _____

Telephone _____

Facsimile _____

Address _____

_____

Post Code _____

Name _____

Telephone _____

Facsimile _____

Address _____

_____

Post Code _____

Name _____

Telephone _____

Facsimile _____

Address _____

_____

Post Code _____

Name _____

Telephone _____

Facsimile _____

Address _____

_____

Post Code _____

Name _____

Telephone _____

Facsimile _____

Address _____

_____

Post Code _____

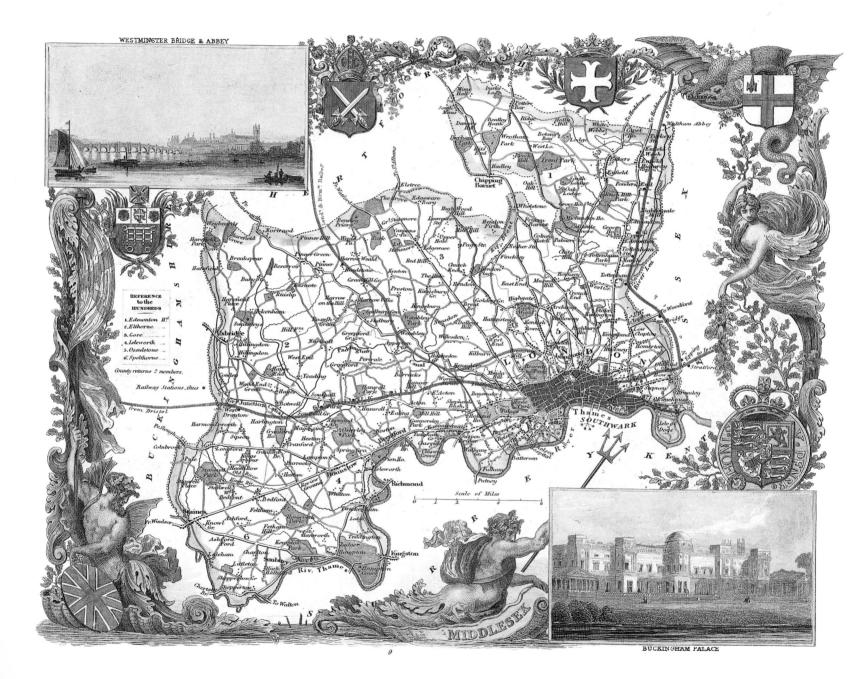

WESTMINSTER BRIDGE & ABBEY

REFERENCE
to the
HUNDREDS
1. Edmonton H^d
2. Elthorne
3. Gore
4. Isleworth
5. Ossulstone
6. Spelthorne

County returns 2 members.

Railway Stations, thus

Scale of Miles

MIDDLESEX

BUCKINGHAM PALACE

NAME / ADDRESS

Name _____

Address _____

Telephone _____

_____

Facsimile _____

Post Code _____

Name _____

Address _____

Telephone _____

_____

Facsimile _____

Post Code _____

Name _____

Address _____

Telephone _____

_____

Facsimile _____

Post Code _____

Name _____

Address _____

Telephone _____

_____

Facsimile _____

Post Code _____

Name _____

Address _____

Telephone _____

_____

Facsimile _____

Post Code _____

NAME /ADDRESS

Name _____ Address _____

Telephone _____ _____

Facsimile _____ _____

_____ Post Code _____

Name _____ Address _____

Telephone _____ _____

Facsimile _____ _____

_____ Post Code _____

Name _____ Address _____

Telephone _____ _____

Facsimile _____ _____

_____ Post Code _____

Name _____ Address _____

Telephone _____ _____

Facsimile _____ _____

_____ Post Code _____

Name _____ Address _____

Telephone _____ _____

Facsimile _____ _____

_____ Post Code _____

NAME/ADDRESS

Name

Telephone

Facsimile

Address

Post Code

Name

Telephone

Facsimile

Address

Post Code

Name

Telephone

Facsimile

Address

Post Code

Name

Telephone

Facsimile

Address

Post Code

Name

Telephone

Facsimile

Address

Post Code

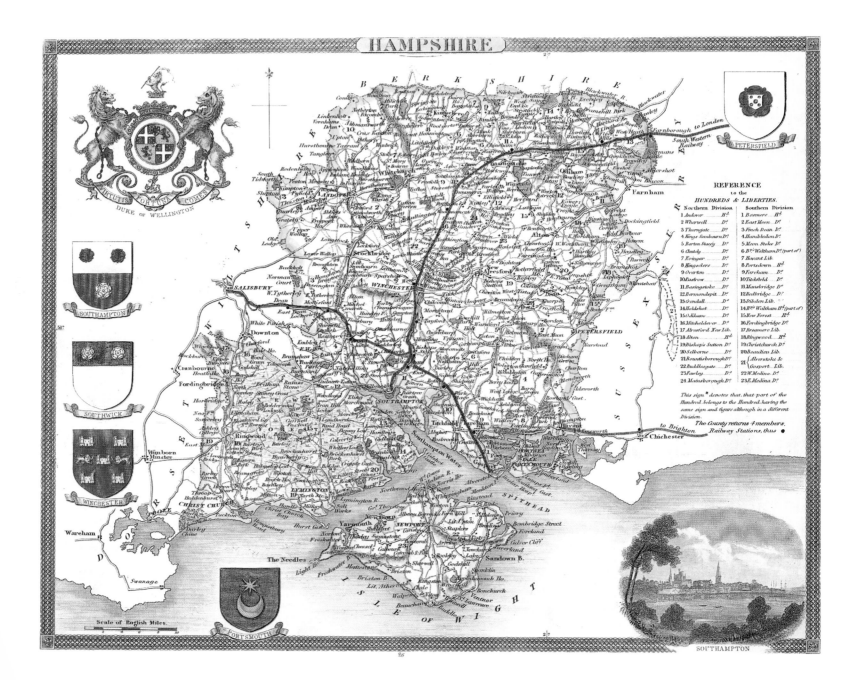

HAMPSHIRE

ARTUTIS FORTUNA COMES
DUKE OF WELLINGTON

SOUTHAMPTON

SOUTHWICK

WINCHESTER

PORTSMOUTH

PETERSFIELD

REFERENCE
to the
HUNDREDS & LIBERTIES.

Northern Division		Southern Division	
1 Andover	Hd	1 Bosmere	Hd
2 Wherwell	Do	2 East Meon	Do
3 Thorngate	Do	3 Finch Dean	Do
4 Kings Somborn	Do	4 Hambledon	Do
5 Barton Stacey	Do	5 Meon Stoke	Do
6 Crudly	Do	6 Bps Waltham Do (part of)	
7 Evinger	Do	7 Havant Lib.	
8 Kingsclere	Do	8 Portsdown	Hd
9 Overton	Do	9 Fareham	Do
10 Eastrow	Do	10 Titchfield	Do
11 Basingstoke	Do	11 Mansbridge	Do
12 Bermondspit	Do	12 Redbridge	Do
13 Crondall	Do	13 Dibden Lib.	
14 Holdshot	Do	14 Bps Waltham Hd (part of)	
15 Odiham	Do	15 New Forest	Hd
16 Micheldever	Do	16 Fordingbridge	Do
17 Alresford New Lib.		17 Breamore Lib.	
18 Alton	Hd	18 Ringwood	Hd
19 Bishop's Sutton	Do	19 Christchurch	Do
20 Selborne	Do	20 Beaulieu Lib.	
21 Bountisborough	Do	21 Alverstoke & Gosport Lib.	
22 Buddlesgate	Do	22 W. Medina	Do
23 Fawley	Do	23 E. Medina	Do
24 Mainsborough	Do		

This sign * denotes that, that part of the
Hundred belongs to the Hundred having the
same sign and figure although, in a different
Division.

The County returns 4 members.

Railway Stations, thus •

SOUTHAMPTON

NAME / ADDRESS

Name _____   Address _____

Telephone _____   _____

Facsimile _____   _____

                                     Post Code _____

Name _____   Address _____

Telephone _____   _____

Facsimile _____   _____

                                     Post Code _____

Name _____   Address _____

Telephone _____   _____

Facsimile _____   _____

                                     Post Code _____

Name _____   Address _____

Telephone _____   _____

Facsimile _____   _____

                                     Post Code _____

Name _____   Address _____

Telephone _____   _____

Facsimile _____   _____

                                     Post Code _____

NAME/ADDRESS

Name _____   Address _____

Telephone _____

Facsimile _____   _____

                                        Post Code _____

Name _____   Address _____

Telephone _____

Facsimile _____   _____

                                        Post Code _____

Name _____   Address _____

Telephone _____

Facsimile _____   _____

                                        Post Code _____

Name _____   Address _____

Telephone _____

Facsimile _____   _____

                                        Post Code _____

Name _____   Address _____

Telephone _____

Facsimile _____   _____

                                        Post Code _____

NAME/ADDRESS

Name   Address

Telephone

Facsimile

                                        Post Code

Name   Address

Telephone

Facsimile

                                        Post Code

Name   Address

Telephone

Facsimile

                                        Post Code

Name   Address

Telephone

Facsimile

                                        Post Code

Name   Address

Telephone

Facsimile

                                        Post Code

Name/Address

Name _____

Telephone _____

Facsimile _____

_____

Address _____

_____

_____

Post Code _____

Name _____

Telephone _____

Facsimile _____

_____

Address _____

_____

_____

Post Code _____

Name _____

Telephone _____

Facsimile _____

_____

Address _____

_____

_____

Post Code _____

Name _____

Telephone _____

Facsimile _____

_____

Address _____

_____

_____

Post Code _____

Name _____

Telephone _____

Facsimile _____

_____

Address _____

_____

_____

Post Code _____

Name /Address

Name

Telephone

Facsimile

Address

Post Code

Name

Telephone

Facsimile

Address

Post Code

Name

Telephone

Facsimile

Address

Post Code

Name

Telephone

Facsimile

Address

Post Code

Name

Telephone

Facsimile

Address

Post Code

Hertfordshire

ST ALBANS ABBEY

CASHIOBURY

Scale of Miles

Railway Stations thus ●

REFERENCE to the HUNDREDS
1. Braughin H⁴
2. Broadwater
3. Cashio
4. Dacorum
5. Edwinstree
6. Hertford
7. Hitchin & Pirton
8. Odsey

NAME /ADDRESS

Name _____   Address _____

Telephone _____   _____

Facsimile _____

_____   Post Code _____

_____

Name _____   Address _____

Telephone _____   _____

Facsimile _____

_____   Post Code _____

_____

Name _____   Address _____

Telephone _____   _____

Facsimile _____

_____   Post Code _____

_____

Name _____   Address _____

Telephone _____   _____

Facsimile _____

_____   Post Code _____

_____

Name _____   Address _____

Telephone _____   _____

Facsimile _____

_____   Post Code _____

Name /Address

Name _____   Address _____

Telephone _____   _____

Facsimile _____

_____   Post Code _____

Name _____   Address _____

Telephone _____   _____

Facsimile _____

_____   Post Code _____

Name _____   Address _____

Telephone _____   _____

Facsimile _____

_____   Post Code _____

Name _____   Address _____

Telephone _____   _____

Facsimile _____

_____   Post Code _____

Name _____   Address _____

Telephone _____   _____

Facsimile _____

_____   Post Code _____

Name /Address

Name

Telephone

Facsimile

Address

Post Code

Name

Telephone

Facsimile

Address

Post Code

Name

Telephone

Facsimile

Address

Post Code

Name

Telephone

Facsimile

Address

Post Code

Name

Telephone

Facsimile

Address

Post Code

CORNWALL

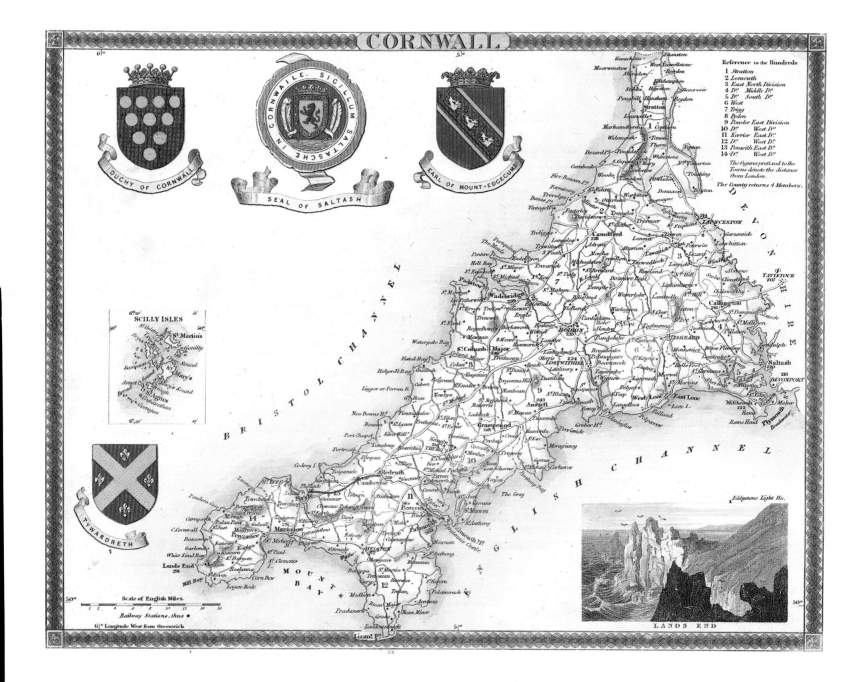

DUCHY OF CORNWALL

SEAL OF SALTASH · SICILLUM SALTASCHE IN CORNWAILE ·

EARL OF MOUNT-EDGECUMB

TYWARDRETH

Reference to the Hundreds

1 Stratton
2 Lesnewth
3 East North Division
4 D° Middle D°
5 D° South D°
6 West
7 Trigg
8 Pyder
9 Powder East Division
10 D° West D°
11 Kerrier East D°
12 D° West D°
13 Penwith East D°
14 D° West D°

The figure prefixed to the Towns denote the distance from London.

The County returns 4 Members.

SCILLY ISLES

St Martins
St Mary's

BRISTOL CHANNEL

DEVONSHIRE

TAVISTOCK 207

CALLINGTON

SALTASH
DEVONPORT

ENGLISH CHANNEL

MOUNT BAY

Lizard Pt

Eddystone Light Ho.

LANDS END

Scale of English Miles.

Railway Stations, thus ●

6° Longitude West from Greenwich

Name /Address

Name

Telephone

Facsimile

Address

Post Code

Name

Telephone

Facsimile

Address

Post Code

Name

Telephone

Facsimile

Address

Post Code

Name

Telephone

Facsimile

Address

Post Code

Name

Telephone

Facsimile

Address

Post Code

Name /Address

Name   Address

Telephone

Facsimile

                                              Post Code

Name   Address

Telephone

Facsimile

                                              Post Code

Name   Address

Telephone

Facsimile

                                              Post Code

Name   Address

Telephone

Facsimile

                                              Post Code

Name   Address

Telephone

Facsimile

                                              Post Code

NAME /ADDRESS

Name

Telephone

Facsimile

Address

Post Code

Name

Telephone

Facsimile

Address

Post Code

Name

Telephone

Facsimile

Address

Post Code

Name

Telephone

Facsimile

Address

Post Code

Name

Telephone

Facsimile

Address

Post Code

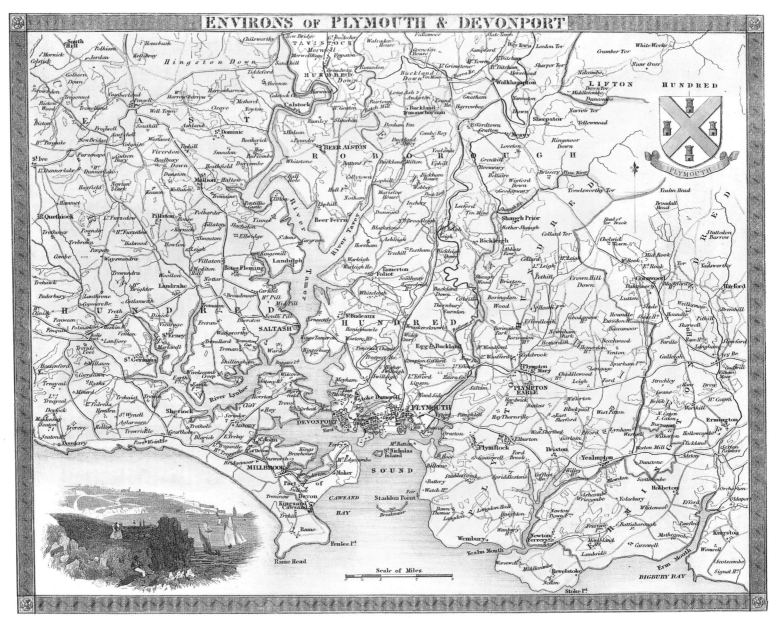

ENVIRONS of PLYMOUTH & DEVONPORT

PLYMOUTH

Scale of Miles.

Engraved for MOULES ENGLISH COUNTIES, by I Dower

NAME / ADDRESS

Name

Address

Telephone

Facsimile

Post Code

Name

Address

Telephone

Facsimile

Post Code

Name

Address

Telephone

Facsimile

Post Code

Name

Address

Telephone

Facsimile

Post Code

Name

Address

Telephone

Facsimile

Post Code

L

NAME / ADDRESS

Name _____   Address _____

Telephone _____   _____

Facsimile _____

_____   Post Code _____

_____   _____

Name _____   Address _____

Telephone _____   _____

Facsimile _____

_____   Post Code _____

_____   _____

Name _____   Address _____

Telephone _____   _____

Facsimile _____

_____   Post Code _____

_____   _____

Name _____   Address _____

Telephone _____   _____

Facsimile _____

_____   Post Code _____

_____   _____

Name _____   Address _____

Telephone _____   _____

Facsimile _____

_____   Post Code _____

NAME / ADDRESS

Name _____

Telephone _____

Facsimile _____

Address _____

_____

Post Code _____

Name _____

Telephone _____

Facsimile _____

Address _____

_____

Post Code _____

Name _____

Telephone _____

Facsimile _____

Address _____

_____

Post Code _____

Name _____

Telephone _____

Facsimile _____

Address _____

_____

Post Code _____

Name _____

Telephone _____

Facsimile _____

Address _____

_____

Post Code _____

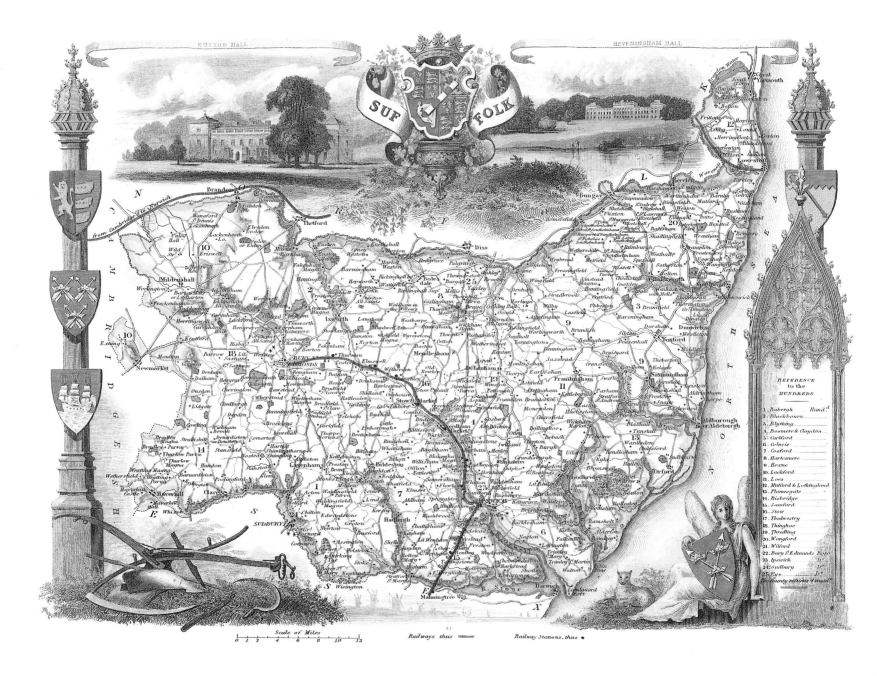

EUSTON HALL.

HEVENINGHAM HALL.

SUF FOLK

Scale of Miles
0 1 2   4   6   8   10   12

Railways thus

Railway Stations, thus

Name/Address

Name

Address

Telephone

Facsimile

Post Code

Name

Address

Telephone

Facsimile

Post Code

Name

Address

Telephone

Facsimile

Post Code

Name

Address

Telephone

Facsimile

Post Code

Name

Address

Telephone

Facsimile

Post Code

M

NAME/ADDRESS

Name _____   Address _____

Telephone _____   _____

Facsimile _____

_____   Post Code _____

Name _____   Address _____

Telephone _____   _____

Facsimile _____

_____   Post Code _____

Name _____   Address _____

Telephone _____   _____

Facsimile _____

_____   Post Code _____

Name _____   Address _____

Telephone _____   _____

Facsimile _____

_____   Post Code _____

Name _____   Address _____

Telephone _____   _____

Facsimile _____

_____   Post Code _____

NAME/ADDRESS

Name _____

Telephone _____

Facsimile _____

Address _____

_____

Post Code _____

Name _____

Telephone _____

Facsimile _____

Address _____

_____

Post Code _____

Name _____

Telephone _____

Facsimile _____

Address _____

_____

Post Code _____

Name _____

Telephone _____

Facsimile _____

Address _____

_____

Post Code _____

Name _____

Telephone _____

Facsimile _____

Address _____

_____

Post Code _____

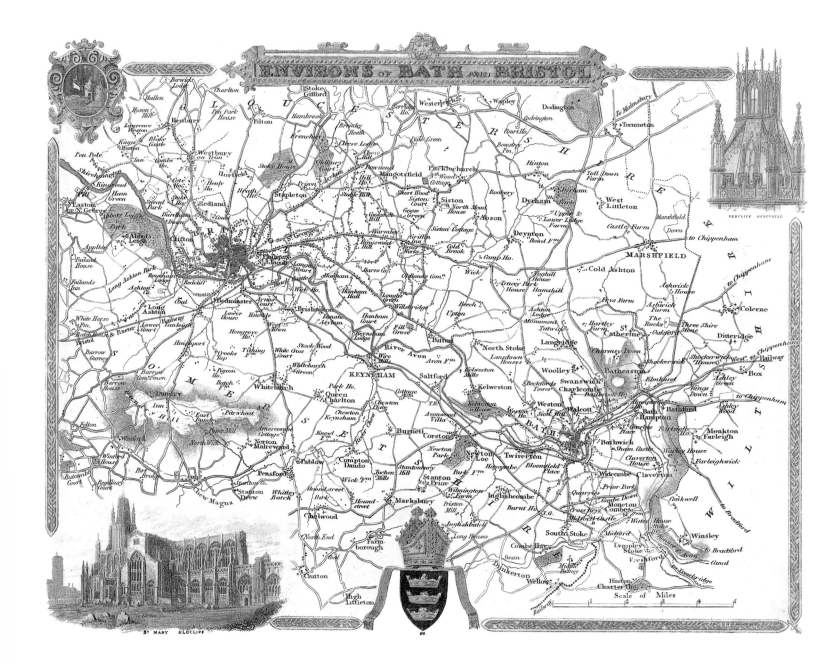

ENVIRONS of BATH and BRISTOL

REDCLIFF RENOVATED

Sᵗ MARY REDCLIFF

Scale of Miles

60

NAME /ADDRESS

Name

Address

Telephone

Facsimile

Post Code

Name

Address

Telephone

Facsimile

Post Code

Name

Address

Telephone

Facsimile

Post Code

Name

Address

Telephone

Facsimile

Post Code

Name

Address

Telephone

Facsimile

Post Code

NAME /ADDRESS

Name _____ Address _____

Telephone _____ _____

Facsimile _____

_____ Post Code _____

_____ _____

Name _____ Address _____

Telephone _____ _____

Facsimile _____

_____ Post Code _____

_____ _____

Name _____ Address _____

Telephone _____ _____

Facsimile _____

_____ Post Code _____

_____ _____

Name _____ Address _____

Telephone _____ _____

Facsimile _____

_____ Post Code _____

_____ _____

Name _____ Address _____

Telephone _____ _____

Facsimile _____

_____ Post Code _____

_____ _____

NAME/ADDRESS

Name

Address

Telephone

Facsimile

Post Code

Name

Address

Telephone

Facsimile

Post Code

Name

Address

Telephone

Facsimile

Post Code

Name

Address

Telephone

Facsimile

Post Code

Name

Address

Telephone

Facsimile

Post Code

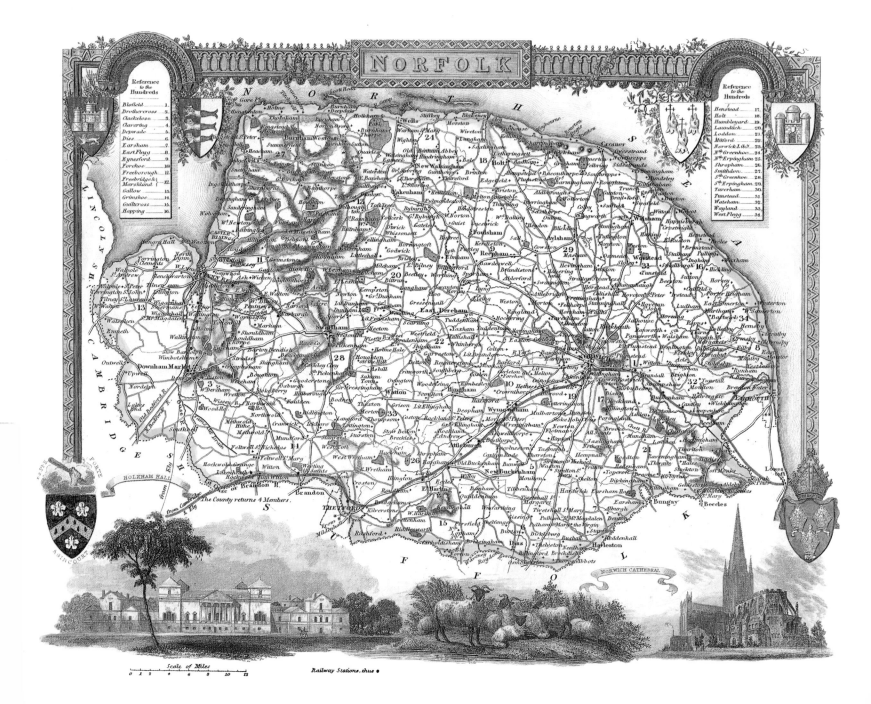

NORFOLK

Reference to the Hundreds

Blofield ... 1
Brothercross ... 2
Clackclose ... 3
Clavering ... 4
Depwade ... 5
Diss ... 6
Earsham ... 7
East Flegg ... 8
Eynesford ... 9
Forehoe ... 10
Freebrough ... 11
Freebridge & Marshland ... 12
Gallow ... 13
Grimshoe ... 14
Guiltcross ... 15
Happing ... 16

Reference to the Hundreds

Henstead ... 17
Holt ... 18
Humbleyard ... 19
Launditch ... 20
Loddon ... 21
Mitford ... 22
Norwick 1 & 9 ... 23
Nth Greenhoe ... 24
Nth Erpingham ... 25
Nth Erpingham ... 26
Shropham ... 27
Smithdon ... 28
Sth Greenhoe ... 28
Sth Erpingham ... 29
Taverham ... 30
Tunstead ... 31
Walsham ... 32
Wayland ... 33
West Flegg ... 34

The County returns 4 Members.

HOLKHAM HALL

NORWICH CATHEDRAL

Scale of Miles
0 1 2   4   6   8   10   12

Railway Stations, thus ●

NAME/ADDRESS

Name   Address

Telephone

Facsimile

                                        Post Code

Name   Address

Telephone

Facsimile

                                        Post Code

Name   Address

Telephone

Facsimile

                                        Post Code

Name   Address

Telephone

Facsimile

                                        Post Code

Name   Address

Telephone

Facsimile

                                        Post Code

O

NAME /ADDRESS

Name _____   Address _____

Telephone _____   _____

Facsimile _____   _____

_____   Post Code _____

_____

Name _____   Address _____

Telephone _____   _____

Facsimile _____   _____

_____   Post Code _____

_____

Name _____   Address _____

Telephone _____   _____

Facsimile _____   _____

_____   Post Code _____

_____

Name _____   Address _____

Telephone _____   _____

Facsimile _____   _____

_____   Post Code _____

_____

Name _____   Address _____

Telephone _____   _____

Facsimile _____   _____

_____   Post Code _____

NAME / ADDRESS

Name

Address

Telephone

Facsimile

Post Code

Name

Address

Telephone

Facsimile

Post Code

Name

Address

Telephone

Facsimile

Post Code

Name

Address

Telephone

Facsimile

Post Code

Name

Address

Telephone

Facsimile

Post Code

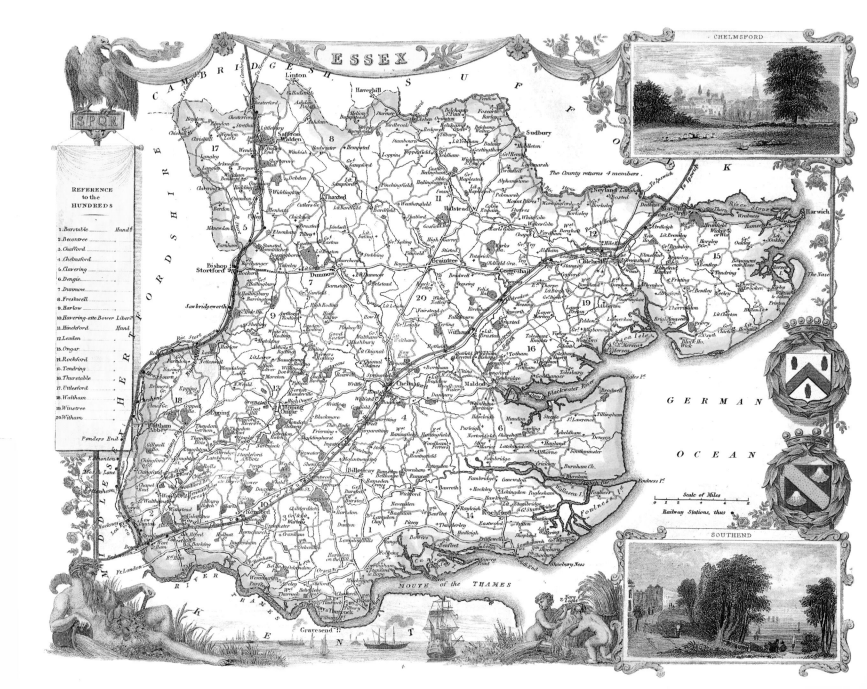

ESSEX

CHELMSFORD

SOUTHEND

REFERENCE
to the
HUNDREDS

1. Barstable .... Hund.
2. Becontree
3. Chafford
4. Chelmsford
5. Clavering
6. Dengie
7. Dunmow
8. Freshwell
9. Harlow
10. Havering-atte-Bower Liber.
11. Hinckford .... Hund.
12. Lexden
13. Ongar
14. Rochford
15. Tendring
16. Thurstable
17. Uttlesford
18. Waltham
19. Winstree
20. Witham

The County returns 4 members.

GERMAN

OCEAN

Scale of Miles

Railway Stations, thus

MOUTH of the THAMES

NAME/ADDRESS

Name

Telephone

Facsimile

Address

Post Code

Name

Telephone

Facsimile

Address

Post Code

Name

Telephone

Facsimile

Address

Post Code

Name

Telephone

Facsimile

Address

Post Code

Name

Telephone

Facsimile

Address

Post Code

P

NAME / ADDRESS

Name   Address

Telephone

Facsimile

                                              Post Code

Name   Address

Telephone

Facsimile

                                              Post Code

Name   Address

Telephone

Facsimile

                                              Post Code

Name   Address

Telephone

Facsimile

                                              Post Code

Name   Address

Telephone

Facsimile

                                              Post Code

NAME /ADDRESS

Name _____ Address _____

Telephone _____ _____

Facsimile _____

_____ Post Code _____

Name _____ Address _____

Telephone _____ _____

Facsimile _____

_____ Post Code _____

Name _____ Address _____

Telephone _____ _____

Facsimile _____

_____ Post Code _____

Name _____ Address _____

Telephone _____ _____

Facsimile _____

_____ Post Code _____

Name _____ Address _____

Telephone _____ _____

Facsimile _____

_____ Post Code _____

NAME /ADDRESS

Name _____ Address _____

Telephone _____ _____

Facsimile _____ _____

Post Code _____

Name _____ Address _____

Telephone _____ _____

Facsimile _____ _____

Post Code _____

Name _____ Address _____

Telephone _____ _____

Facsimile _____ _____

Post Code _____

Name _____ Address _____

Telephone _____ _____

Facsimile _____ _____

Post Code _____

Name _____ Address _____

Telephone _____ _____

Facsimile _____ _____

Post Code _____

NAME /ADDRESS

Name _____

Telephone _____

Facsimile _____

Address _____

_____

Post Code _____

Name _____

Telephone _____

Facsimile _____

Address _____

_____

Post Code _____

Name _____

Telephone _____

Facsimile _____

Address _____

_____

Post Code _____

Name _____

Telephone _____

Facsimile _____

Address _____

_____

Post Code _____

Name _____

Telephone _____

Facsimile _____

Address _____

_____

Post Code _____

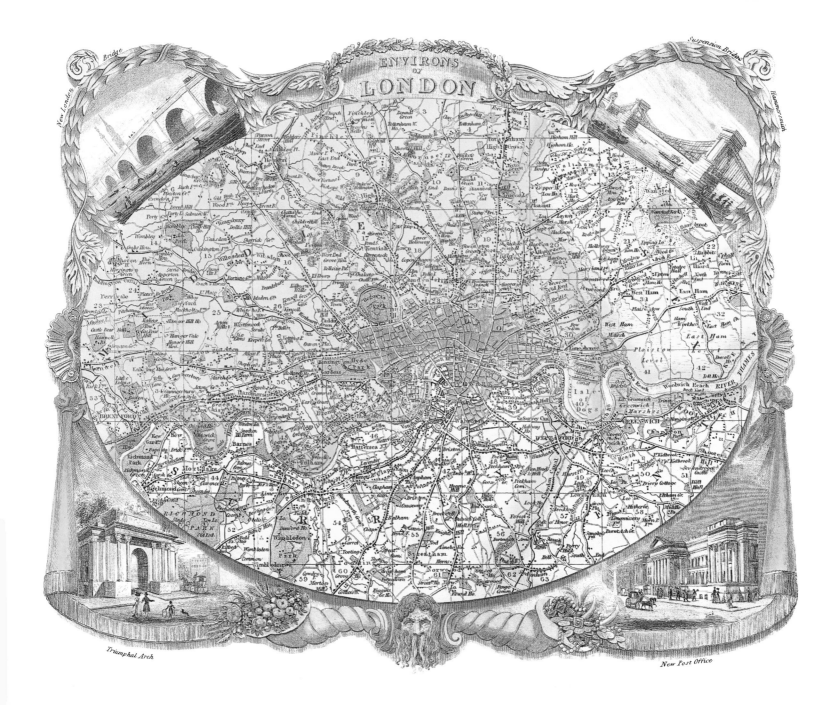

ENVIRONS OF LONDON

Bridge

New London

Suspension Bridge

Hammersmith

Triumphal Arch

New Post Office

NAME/ADDRESS

Name

Address

Telephone

Facsimile

Post Code

Name

Address

Telephone

Facsimile

Post Code

Name

Address

Telephone

Facsimile

Post Code

Name

Address

Telephone

Facsimile

Post Code

R

Name

Address

Telephone

Facsimile

Post Code

NAME /ADDRESS

Name _____

Telephone _____

Facsimile _____

Address _____

_____

Post Code _____

Name _____

Telephone _____

Facsimile _____

Address _____

_____

Post Code _____

Name _____

Telephone _____

Facsimile _____

Address _____

_____

Post Code _____

Name _____

Telephone _____

Facsimile _____

Address _____

_____

Post Code _____

Name _____

Telephone _____

Facsimile _____

Address _____

_____

Post Code _____

Name /Address

Name

Telephone

Facsimile

Address

Post Code

Name

Telephone

Facsimile

Address

Post Code

Name

Telephone

Facsimile

Address

Post Code

Name

Telephone

Facsimile

Address

Post Code

Name

Telephone

Facsimile

Address

Post Code

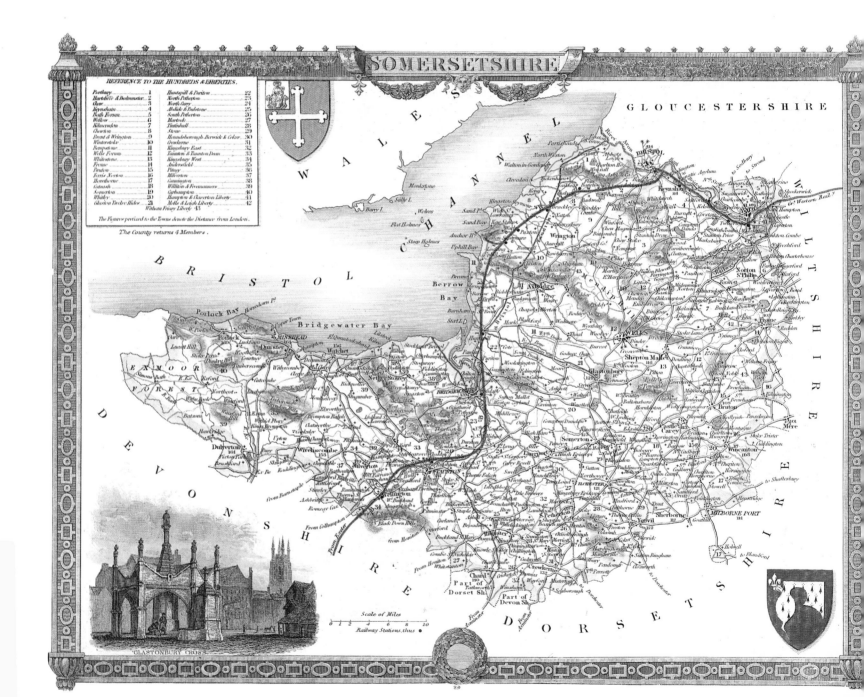

SOMERSETSHIRE

GLOUCESTERSHIRE

WALES

BRISTOL CHANNEL

BRISTOL

WILTSHIRE

Great Western Railway

Portlock Bay

Bridgewater Bay

Berrow Bay

BRISTOL

MENDIP

EXMOOR FOREST

MINEHEAD
Dunster

WELLS

Shepton Mallet

Glastonbury

BRIDGEWATER

DEVONSHIRE

Dulverton

Wiveliscombe

Somerton

Wellington

ILCHESTER

Sherborne

MILBORNE PORT

Wincanton

Yeovil

Crewkerne

Chard

Part of Dorset Sh.

Part of Devon Sh.

DORSETSHIRE

Scale of Miles
0 1 2 4 6 8 10
Railway Stations, thus •

"GLASTONBURY CROSS"

29

Name /Address

Name _____   Address _____

Telephone _____   _____

Facsimile _____   _____

_____   Post Code _____

Name _____   Address _____

Telephone _____   _____

Facsimile _____   _____

_____   Post Code _____

Name _____   Address _____

Telephone _____   _____

Facsimile _____   _____

_____   Post Code _____

Name _____   Address _____

Telephone _____   _____

Facsimile _____   _____

_____   Post Code _____

Name _____   Address _____

Telephone _____   _____

Facsimile _____   _____

_____   Post Code _____

S

Name /Address

Name

Telephone

Facsimile

Address

Post Code

Name

Telephone

Facsimile

Address

Post Code

Name

Telephone

Facsimile

Address

Post Code

Name

Telephone

Facsimile

Address

Post Code

Name

Telephone

Facsimile

Address

Post Code

Name /Address

Name

Telephone

Facsimile

Address

Post Code

Name

Telephone

Facsimile

Address

Post Code

Name

Telephone

Facsimile

Address

Post Code

Name

Telephone

Facsimile

Address

Post Code

Name

Telephone

Facsimile

Address

Post Code

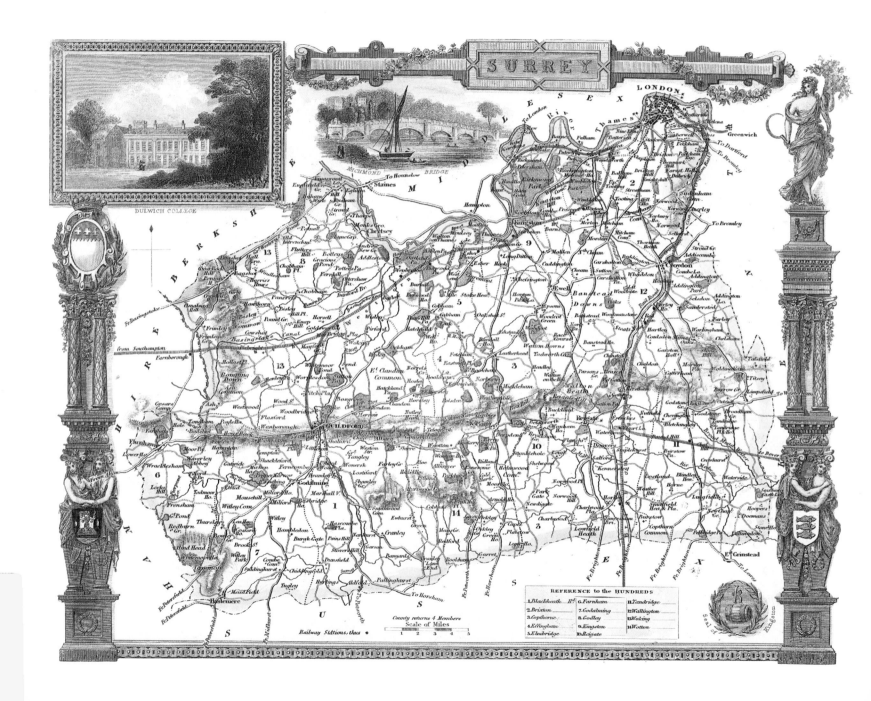

SURREY

DULWICH COLLEGE

RICHMOND BRIDGE

REFERENCE to the HUNDREDS

1. Blackheath Hd.   6. Farnham   11. Tandridge
2. Brixton   7. Godalming   12. Wallington
3. Copthorne   8. Godley   13. Woking
4. Effingham   9. Kingston   14. Wotton
5. Elmbridge   10. Reigate

County returns 4 Members
Scale of Miles
1 2 3 4 5

Railway Stations, thus

NAME / ADDRESS

Name

Address

Telephone

Facsimile

Post Code

Name

Address

Telephone

Facsimile

Post Code

Name

Address

Telephone

Facsimile

Post Code

Name

Address

Telephone

Facsimile

Post Code

Name

Address

Telephone

Facsimile

Post Code

T

NAME/ADDRESS

Name _____ Address _____

Telephone _____

Facsimile _____ _____

_____ Post Code _____

Name _____ Address _____

Telephone _____

Facsimile _____ _____

_____ Post Code _____

Name _____ Address _____

Telephone _____

Facsimile _____ _____

_____ Post Code _____

Name _____ Address _____

Telephone _____

Facsimile _____ _____

_____ Post Code _____

Name _____ Address _____

Telephone _____

Facsimile _____ _____

_____ Post Code _____

NAME /ADDRESS

Name   Address

Telephone

Facsimile

                                                Post Code

Name   Address

Telephone

Facsimile

                                                Post Code

Name   Address

Telephone

Facsimile

                                                Post Code

Name   Address

Telephone

Facsimile

                                                Post Code

Name   Address

Telephone

Facsimile

                                                Post Code

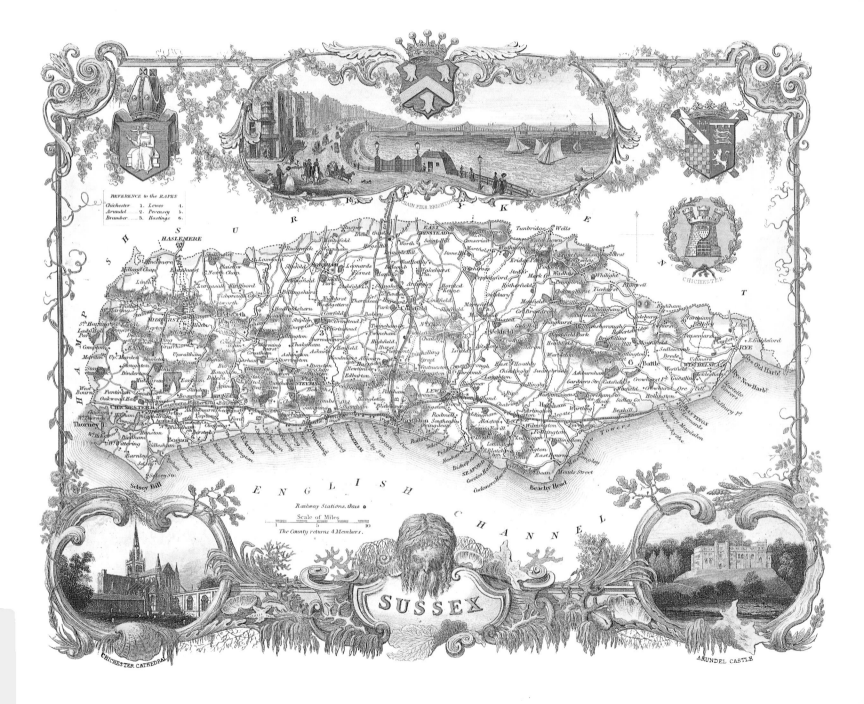

SUSSEX

CHICHESTER CATHEDRAL

ARUNDEL CASTLE

REFERENCE to the RAPES

Chichester	1.	Lewes	4.
Arundel	2.	Pevensey	5.
Bramber	3.	Hastings	6.

CHAIN PIER, BRIGHTON.

CHICHESTER

Railway Stations, thus ⊙

Scale of Miles

10

The County returns 4 Members.

ENGLISH CHANNEL

Name /Address

Name		Address	
Telephone			
Facsimile			
		Post Code	

Name		Address	
Telephone			
Facsimile			
		Post Code	

Name		Address	
Telephone			
Facsimile			
		Post Code	

Name		Address	
Telephone			
Facsimile			
		Post Code	

Name		Address	
Telephone			
Facsimile			
		Post Code	

UV

NAME/ADDRESS

Name

Telephone

Facsimile

Address

Post Code

Name

Telephone

Facsimile

Address

Post Code

Name

Telephone

Facsimile

Address

Post Code

Name

Telephone

Facsimile

Address

Post Code

Name

Telephone

Facsimile

Address

Post Code

NAME /ADDRESS

Name _____ Address _____

Telephone _____ _____

Facsimile _____ _____

_____ Post Code _____

Name _____ Address _____

Telephone _____ _____

Facsimile _____ _____

_____ Post Code _____

Name _____ Address _____

Telephone _____ _____

Facsimile _____ _____

_____ Post Code _____

Name _____ Address _____

Telephone _____ _____

Facsimile _____ _____

_____ Post Code _____

Name _____ Address _____

Telephone _____ _____

Facsimile _____ _____

_____ Post Code _____

ISLE OF WIGHT

REFERENCE

West Medina 1
East D⁰. 2

The County returns 1 member:

LYMINGTON

Portsmouth Harbour

GOSPORT · PORTSEA · PORTS-MOUTH

Haslar Hospital

S.ᵗ Sea Castle

SPITHEAD

THE SOLENT

Gurnet Bay

Norris Castle

Mother Bank

Kings Quay

Binsted

HYDE

Appley

RYDE

St Johns

Sea View · Old Fort

Nettlestone Pt

Priory · Watch House Pt

St Helens

Bembridge Pt

Brading Har

Foreland

White Cliff Bay

Culver Cliff

SANDOWN BAY

YARMOUTH

Cliffs End

Colwell Bay

How Ledge

Tollands Bay

Hatherwood Point

Allum Bay

The Needles

Light House

NEWPORT

Parkhurst

Carisbrooke

Calbourn

Brixton

Kingston

Godshill

Shanklin

Shanklin Chine

Dunnose

Luccomb Chine

Chine Head

Bonchurch

Blackgang Chine

Bay

Chale

Scale of Miles

CARISBROOKE CASTLE

90

NAME /ADDRESS

Name

Telephone

Facsimile

Address

Post Code

Name

Telephone

Facsimile

Address

Post Code

Name

Telephone

Facsimile

Address

Post Code

Name

Telephone

Facsimile

Address

Post Code

Name

Telephone

Facsimile

Address

Post Code

NAME / ADDRESS

Name _____ Address _____

Telephone _____

Facsimile _____ _____

_____ Post Code _____

Name _____ Address _____

Telephone _____

Facsimile _____ _____

_____ Post Code _____

Name _____ Address _____

Telephone _____

Facsimile _____ _____

_____ Post Code _____

Name _____ Address _____

Telephone _____

Facsimile _____ _____

_____ Post Code _____

Name _____ Address _____

Telephone _____

Facsimile _____ _____

_____ Post Code _____

NAME /ADDRESS

Name _____ Address _____

Telephone _____ _____

Facsimile _____

_____ Post Code _____

Name _____ Address _____

Telephone _____ _____

Facsimile _____

_____ Post Code _____

Name _____ Address _____

Telephone _____ _____

Facsimile _____

_____ Post Code _____

Name _____ Address _____

Telephone _____ _____

Facsimile _____

_____ Post Code _____

Name _____ Address _____

Telephone _____ _____

Facsimile _____

_____ Post Code _____

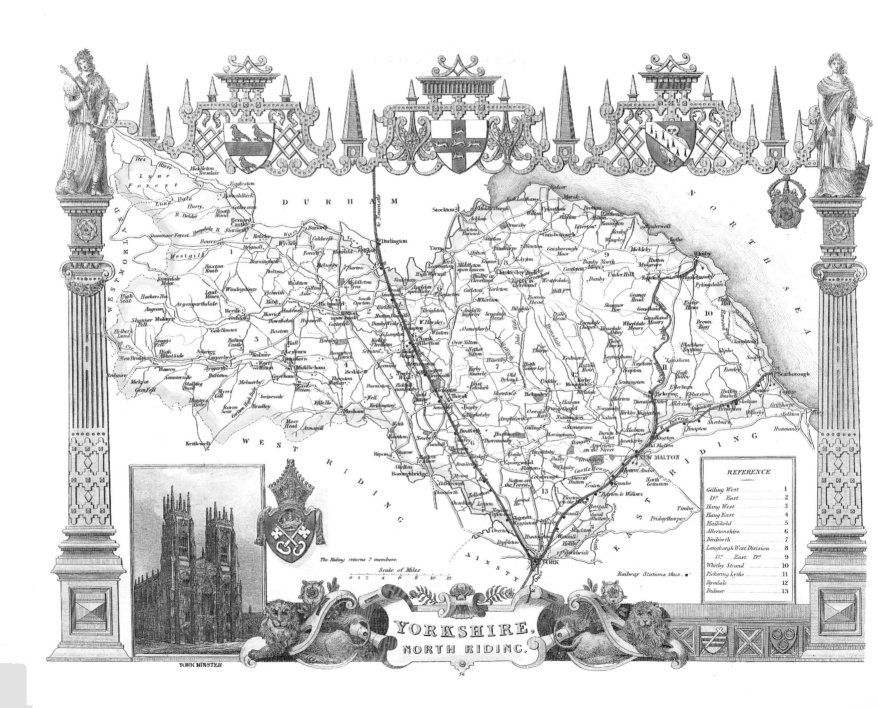

YORKSHIRE,
NORTH RIDING.

YORK MINSTER

REFERENCE.

Gilling West	1
D.º East	2
Hang West	3
Hang East	4
Halikeld	5
Allertonshire	6
Birdforth	7
Langbargh West Division	8
D.º East D.º	9
Whitby Strand	10
Pickering Lythe	11
Ryedale	12
Bulmer	13

The Riding returns 2 members.

Scale of Miles

0 2 4 6 8 10 12

Railway Stations, thus

DURHAM

WESTMORLAND

WEST RIDING

EAST RIDING

NORTH SEA

AINSTY

NAME /ADDRESS

Name

Telephone

Facsimile

Address

Post Code

Name

Telephone

Facsimile

Address

Post Code

Name

Telephone

Facsimile

Address

Post Code

Name

Telephone

Facsimile

Address

Post Code

Name

Telephone

Facsimile

Address

Post Code

XYZ

Name /Address

Name

Telephone

Facsimile

Address

Post Code

Name

Telephone

Facsimile

Address

Post Code

Name

Telephone

Facsimile

Address

Post Code

Name

Telephone

Facsimile

Address

Post Code

Name

Telephone

Facsimile

Address

Post Code

NAME /ADDRESS

Name

Telephone

Facsimile

Address

Post Code

Name

Telephone

Facsimile

Address

Post Code

Name

Telephone

Facsimile

Address

Post Code

Name

Telephone

Facsimile

Address

Post Code

Name

Telephone

Facsimile

Address

Post Code

NAME/ADDRESS

Name _____   Address _____

Telephone _____

Facsimile _____

    Post Code _____

_____

Name _____   Address _____

Telephone _____

Facsimile _____

    Post Code _____

_____

Name _____   Address _____

Telephone _____

Facsimile _____

    Post Code _____

_____

Name _____   Address _____

Telephone _____

Facsimile _____

    Post Code _____

_____

Name _____   Address _____

Telephone _____

Facsimile _____

    Post Code _____

Carnedd Lewellyn N.W. 3469

Carnedd David N.W. 3427

Ben. Mou N.B. 3500

Crudchen Ben N.B. 3400

Snowden the Highest Hill in N.W. 3571

Schehalt N.B. 350

High Point 3166

Low Point 3092

Sea Fell Cumberland the Highest Hill in England

Skiddaw Cumb! 3082

Ben Lomond N.B. 3262

Lvellyn 3053 Cumberland

The Pillar Cumb.d 2893

Bow Fell. Cumb.d 2911

Cadir Idris N.W. 2914

Arra N.W

Cross Fell Cumb.d 2901

Beacons 2862 Brecon. the highest Hills in S.W.

Saddleback Cumb! 2787

Cheviot N.B. 2658

Grasmere Fell Cumb.d 2756

Coniston Fell Lancas.r 2577

Cadir Terwyn N.W. 2563

Cradle S.W. 2543

Dunras N.B. 2409

Capellant S.W. 2394

Hedgehope Northumb.d 2347

Plynlimm S.W. 246

Trecastle S.W. 2596

Whernside in Ingleton Fells Yorksh. 2384

Water Crag Yorksh. 2186

Queensbury Hill N.B. 2259

Carn Fell 2245 Yorksh.

Kilpope Law Durham 2196

Wh Kettle Yor

Shunner Fell Yorksh. 2329

Snea Fell Isle of Man 2004

9 Standards Westmorland 2136

Ingleborough Yorksh. 2361

Penningent Yorksh. 2270

Dwygat Brecon 2071

High Peak Cumber.d 210

Black Comb Cumber.d 1919

Ho Derbysh. 185

or Forest W. 2163

Yorkshire Proverb "Pendal, Ingleboro, and Penningent Are the Highest Hills between Scotland & Trent"

North Berule Isle of Man

Dunkerry B the Highest West of Engla

sand Beacon evon. 1792

Gerwyn Goch N.W. 1722

Pendal Hill Lancashire 1803

Axedge Derbyshire 1751

Longmount Forest Salop. 1674

Llangunor S.W. 1659

Myvold. Maur Monmouthsh. 1568

Penmaen Mawr N.W. 1540

Rippan Tor Devon 1549

Malvern 1444

Tilden Hills N.B. 1364

Wrekin Salop. 1320

Mamtorr Derbysh. 1300 one of the Won ders of the Peak

Stow Hill Hi Herefordshire

rsedge shire 7

Black Hambledown Yorksh. 1246

Moeltra Arst Denbighsh. 1037

Broadway Beacon 1086

Weaver Hill 1151 Staffordshire

Bu Dev

Bradley Knoll Somerset 913

White Horse Hill Berks 892

Leiths Hill Surry 993

Botley Hill Surry 830

Hind Hill 992 Surry

Epwell Hill Oxfordsh. 836

Nettlebed Windmill Oxfordsh. 820

Rooks Hill 702 Surry

Hollingborn Kent 616

Shotover Oxford 599

Stockbridge Hants 620

Banstead Downs Surry 576

Norwood Hills 370

Shooters Hill 446 Kent